C000126910

Clarinet
Initial

Pieces
for Trinity College London exams

2017-2020

Published by
Trinity College London Press
trinitycollege.com

Registered in England
Company no. 09726123

Copyright © 2016 Trinity College London Press
First impression, September 2016

Printed in England by Caligraving Ltd.

Evening Song

ed. Jack Brymer

Madeleine Dring
(1923-1977)

poco rit.

molto rit.

Pony Ride

Paul Harris

Stillness

James Rae
(born 1957)

Slowly and expressively [♩ = 92–100]

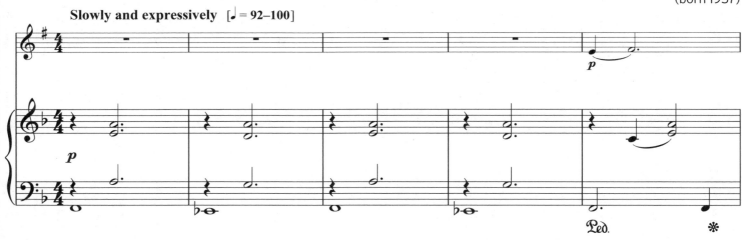

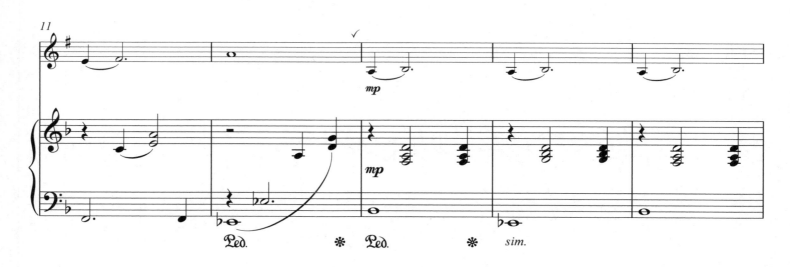

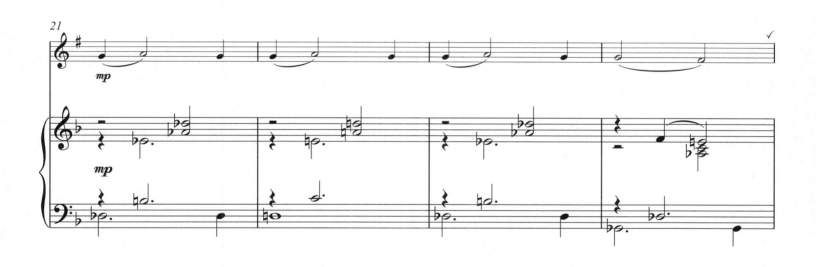

Scarborough Fair

arr. Mark Mumford

Traditional

Clarinet
Initial

Pieces
for Trinity College London exams

2017-2020

Published by
Trinity College London Press
trinitycollege.com

Registered in England
Company no. 09726123

TCL 015983
ISBN 978-0-85736-551-4

Evening Song

ed. Jack Brymer

Madeleine Dring
(1923-1977)

Pony Ride

Paul Harris

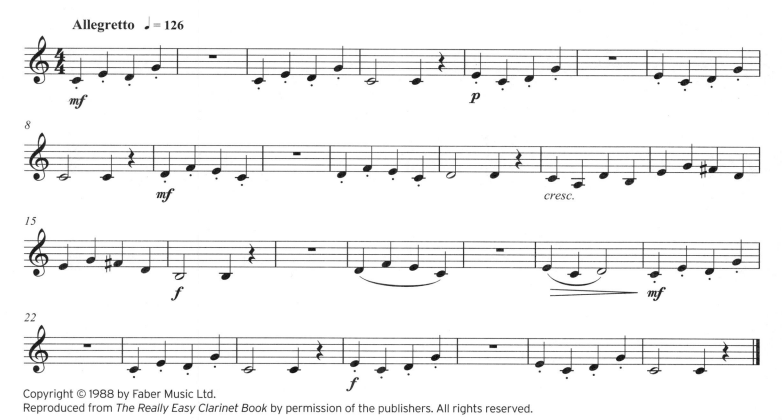

Stillness

James Rae
(born 1957)

Scarborough Fair

arr. Mark Mumford

Traditional

The Birch Tree

arr. Paul Harris

Traditional Russian

Puff the Magic Dragon

arr. Mark Mumford

Peter Yarrow (born 1938)
and Leonard Lipton (born 1940)

Across Chelsea Bridge

Philip Sparke
(born 1951)

I'm Bound Away

arr. Chris Walters

Traditional Sea Shanty

Whistle While You Walk

Kim Cleaton
(born 1986)

The Birch Tree

arr. Paul Harris

Traditional Russian

Puff the Magic Dragon

arr. Mark Mumford

Peter Yarrow (born 1938)
and Leonard Lipton (born 1940)